Jesus Loves You, No Matter What!

Trilogy Christian Publishers
A Wholly Owned Subsidiary of Trinity Broadcasting Network
2442 Michelle Drive
Tustin, CA 92780

For information, address Trilogy Christian Publishing
Rights Department, 2442 Michelle Drive, Tustin, Ca 92780.
Trilogy Christian Publishing/ TBN and colophon are trademarks of Trinity Broadcasting Network.

For information about special discounts for bulk purchases, please contact Trilogy Christian Publishing.

Manufactured in the United States of America

10 9 8 7 6 5 4 3 2 1

Library of Congress Cataloging-in-Publication Data is available.

ISBN 978-1-64773-784-9 (Print Book)
ISBN 978-1-64773-785-6 (ebook)

Jesus Loves You, No Matter What!

LINDA RADELLA

WELCOME
Miss Shirley's
Sunday School

Gma: Hello, children! My name is Gma, short for Grandma. It is a nickname.

Do you have a nickname? Sometimes I call my grandchildren Sweetie or Pumpkin or even Dude.

I am a helper in this class. I help the teacher. I also help the children.

Today I am going to tell you a story about Timmy. He is four years old and lives with his mom. Timmy's dad is in the military overseas.

Mom: Timmy, please put your toys away now and get ready for church.

Timmy: I don't want to go to church! I want to play.

Mom: You can play when we get back from church. Now, hurry and get ready.

Timmy: I do not want to go to church. I want to play with my cars. I should not have to go to church if I don't want to.

Timmy: Mom, I do not want to go to church.

Mom: You will enjoy going to Sunday school. You will see. Once you get there, you will feel better.

Timmy: I guess.

Ms. Shirley: Welcome, Timmy! Glad you could join us today. Would you please join the other children in the play area?

Gma: Hi, Timmy! It is good to see you again. Welcome!

Ms. Shirley: Okay, children. It is time to put the toys away and get ready to sing songs to Jesus.

Timmy: I want to play. I don't want to sing.

Gma: Timmy, do you need help putting the toys away? I can help you.

Timmy: I want to play some more.

Gma: Everyone must put the toys away and get ready to sing.

Timmy: I don't want to sing.

Ms. Shirley: Timmy, please put away the toys and join the others. Thank you.

The Lord is my SHEPHERD
I AM A CHILD OF GOD

Birthdays

Ms. Shirley: Today we are going to sing "Jesus Loves the Little Children." Who remembers the words?

Gma: Timmy, did you forget the song? I can help you.

Ms. Shirley: Okay, children, let us start. "Jesus loves the little children…"

Ms. Shirley: Timmy, I did not hear you singing. Please put your toy away and sing with us.

Gma: Can I help you with the words, Timmy?

Timmy: *Saying it loudly,* No, I don't want to sing! I miss my daddy. I want to go home!

Ms. Shirley: Okay, Timmy. Since you do not want to sing, please go to the time-out chair until we are finished.

Gma: Timmy, I want you to know that Jesus loves you, no matter what. He is with you always, and He wants you to be happy. He knows you miss your daddy, but he is doing a great thing defending our country.

Timmy: Well, I am not happy, and so Jesus must not be with me.

Gma: *Chuckling,* Jesus gives us His Word, His promise, to be with us always. No matter how we feel—mad, sad, happy, angry—He is still with us, no matter what. Would you like me and you to pray and ask Jesus to help you feel happier?

Timmy: Jesus won't want me. I get mad. I don't listen.

Gma: Jesus loves you, no matter what! He promises, and He never breaks a promise. Let's pray together.

Timmy: *Meekly,* Okay.

The Lord
is my
SHEPHERD
I AM A
CHILD OF
GOD

Gma: Dear Jesus…

Timmy: Dear Jesus…

Gma: Thank You…

Timmy: Thank you…

Gma: For loving me, no matter what!

Timmy: For loving me, no matter what!

Gma: I am sorry.

Timmy: I am sorry.

Gma: Help me be better, Jesus.

Timmy: Help me be better, Jesus.

Gma: Amen.

Timmy: Amen.

Ms. Shirley: You can join us now, Timmy. We are going to make a globe for our craft.

The Lord
is my
SHEPHERD

Ms. Shirley: *To Gma,* Timmy is in a much better mood now.

Gma: Yes, he just needed some time with Jesus in prayer.

Ms. Shirley: Jesus always makes the difference.

Gma: He sure does! Jesus loves us, no matter what!

Gma: I hope you enjoyed Timmy's story. Jesus does make the difference! Do you know about Jesus? He is God's one and only Son. God loves us so much that He sent Jesus to tell us all about God's love for us. God wants to adopt us into His big, big family. All you have to do is believe and say yes. Here is a prayer that may help: God, I know that You made me and love me. I have bad thoughts sometimes and have done things I know are wrong. I am sorry and ask You to forgive me. I know that Jesus came from heaven to tell us about You and all of Your promises. Thank You! I love You too. Amen. Welcome to the family!

CPSIA information can be obtained
at www.ICGtesting.com
Printed in the USA
BVHW020000190521
607645BV00007B/1029